Ancient Greek Myths

Created and designed by
David Salariya

BOOK HOUSE

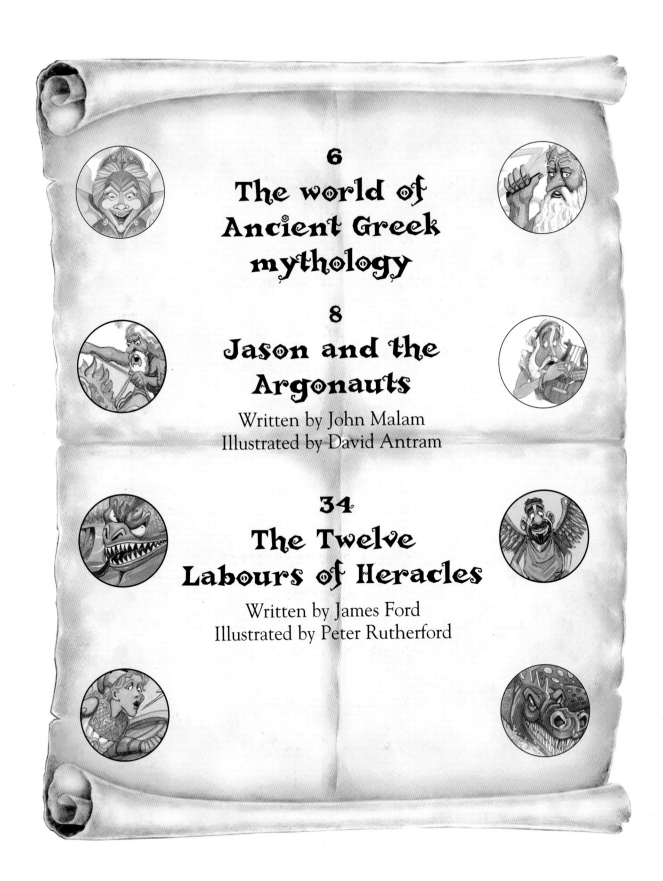

Ancient
Greek
Myths

Authors:
James Ford
Peter Hepplewhite
John Malam
Sue Reid

Illustrators:
David Antram
Mark Bergin
Peter Rutherford

Series Creator:
David Salariya

Editor:
Michael Ford

Editorial Assistant:
Mark Williams

Previous edition © 2004, 2005
The Salariya Book Company Ltd:

Jason and the Argonauts (2005)
HB ISBN-10: 1-904642-35-7
PB ISBN-10: 1-904642-36-5

The Twelve Labours of Heracles (2005)
HB ISBN-10: 1-904642-33-0
PB ISBN-10: 1-904642-34-9

The Wooden Horse of Troy (2004)
HB ISBN-10: 1-904642-29-2
PB ISBN-10: 1-904642-30-6

The Voyages of Odysseus (2004)
HB ISBN-10: 1-904642-31-4
PB ISBN-10: 1-904642-32-2

The Adventures of Perseus (2004)
HB ISBN-10: 1-904642-25-X
PB ISBN-10: 1-904642-26-8

Published in Great Britain in 2008 by
Book House, an imprint of
The Salariya Book Company Ltd
25 Marlborough Place, Brighton BN1 1UB
www.salariya.com
www.book-house.co.uk

HB ISBN-13: 978-1-906370-35-0
PB ISBN-13: 978-1-906370-37-4

SALARIYA

A CIP catalogue record for this book is available
from the British Library.

Printed and bound in China.
Printed on paper from sustainable sources.

PAPER FROM
SUSTAINABLE
FORESTS

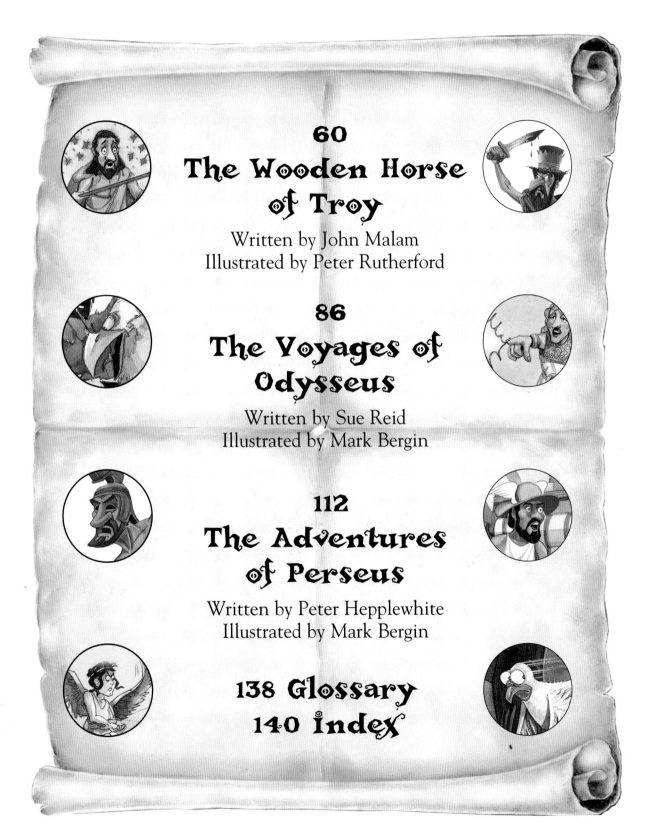

The world of Ancient Greek mythology

The Ancient Greek civilisation was one of the greatest the world has ever witnessed. It reached its peak of success in the 400s BC – nearly 2,500 years ago.

We owe much to the Ancient Greeks. They were great scientists, mathematicians, writers and thinkers. They were also brilliant storytellers. Many of the tales they told were in the form of poems, often thousands of lines long. The Greeks wrote poems about many kinds of human experience, such as love, friendship, war, revenge, history, and even simple everyday activities such as farming. The most famous of the poems which have passed down to us are epic tales of courage and warfare, where gods, heroes and monsters struggle against great odds.

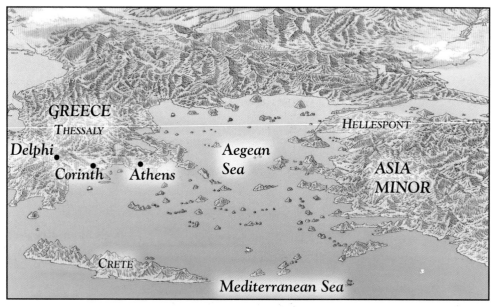

A map showing the Ancient Greek mainland, surrounding islands and neighbouring lands

GREECE
THESSALY
Delphi
Corinth
Athens
CRETE
Aegean Sea
HELLESPONT
ASIA MINOR
Mediterranean Sea

At first, the Greeks had no writing. All of their stories, lengthy as they were, were handed down from generation to generation by word of mouth. The people who told them were often travelling storytellers who performed in towns throughout the Greek world. They were called *rhapsodes*, which means 'song-stitchers'. As a rhapsode spoke or sang the words of his story, in a loud and clear voice, he stitched its many twists and turns together to make a beginning, a middle and an end. He would invent many details, cruel or comic, to make the story more lively. But he would have to be careful what he said about the immortal gods, because if they were offended they could inflict terrible punishments on helpless mortals.

Gods, heroes and mortals

The Ancient Greeks believed in gods and goddesses who were, in some ways, just like humans. They had adventures, fell in love, had children. Like people, they felt anger, love, hatred, jealousy, friendship. But unlike people they were immortal, and eternally young. Living a life of luxury on the summit of Mount Olympus, they never felt hunger, thirst or tiredness. They had supernatural powers: they could travel to distant places in no time at all, control the elements, make themselves invisible or disguise themselves whenever they liked.

Between the gods and ordinary mortals were what the Greeks called heroes. Heroes were mortal, but they were stronger, braver or cleverer than ordinary people, and they were destined for great adventures. Some of them were demigods, the offspring of a god and a mortal – for mortal women were sometimes so beautiful that even the gods fell in love with them. Heracles, the greatest hero of all, was himself worshipped as a god after his death.

The rhapsode often accompanied himself on the lyre. The Ancient Greeks believed that this instrument was invented by the god Hermes.

Eventually these wonderful stories were written down, and we can still read them today. This book retells five of the best-known tales, but remember that what you read here is just one version of the story – some myths existed in several different versions, depending on who told the story and who was in the audience. Enjoy them – they are some of the greatest tales ever told.

Jason and the Argonauts

Meet the heroes

Jason
Son of a king, brought up by a centaur, Jason is promised that he can be king himself if he brings back the Golden Fleece.

Heracles
The mighty hero Heracles (or Hercules, as the Romans call him) takes time out from his twelve labours to sail with Jason.

Pelias
Jason's wicked uncle has seized the royal throne for himself. But how long will he be able to hold on to it?

Orpheus
Son of the muse Calliope, Orpheus is the greatest poet and singer in the Greek world. His music can even tame wild beasts.

Chiron
Half-man, half-horse, the centaur Chiron may look wild, but he is wise and gentle and a great teacher.

Medea
The daughter of King Aeetes of Colchis is a fearsome sorceress. She falls in love with Jason, but will they live happily ever after?

Introduction

Greetings, citizens. Gather round. I am the rhapsode – the teller of stories. My tale is about a boy born to be king, whose birthright was cruelly taken from him. His name was Jason, and his future lay across dangerous seas in the faraway land of Colchis. There he would find the fabulous Golden Fleece – the dazzling skin of a flying, talking ram. His mission was to seize the Fleece and return with it. If he was successful, he would be made king. However, once Jason's ship was out of sight, no-one thought they would ever see him alive again. Lend me your ears!

I come this day from far away
With a tale to tell that spins a spell,
Which you will hear – if you draw near –
Of times of old and heroes bold.

So gather round and hear my story
Which I will weave from ancient glory,
By joining threads from start to end –
Then you may pass it to a friend.

There was a boy named Jason...

My story begins in a town in Greece called Iolcus. It lay on the coast of the Aegean Sea, in the kingdom of Thessaly. Iolcus had been founded by King Cretheus. He promised that when he died, his son, Aeson, would inherit the throne and become the next king.

Cretheus had another son, Pelias. He was Aeson's younger half-brother. Unknown to Aeson, Pelias wanted to be the next king. When their father died, Pelias seized his chance and declared himself the new ruler of Iolcus. Fearing he might be surrounded by enemies, Pelias consulted an oracle which predicted his future. For stealing the throne of Iolcus, Pelias learned that one day he would be killed by a descendant of the royal family. Cruel Pelias tried to change the future. He murdered the royal family, so there would be no-one left to come after him. Last of all, Pelias went after the son of Aeson and Alcimede – a baby boy named Jason.

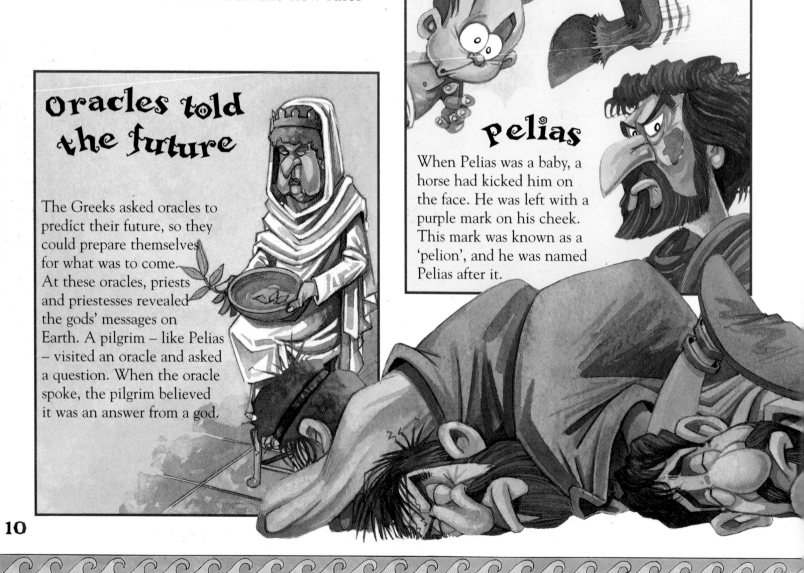

Oracles told the future

The Greeks asked oracles to predict their future, so they could prepare themselves for what was to come. At these oracles, priests and priestesses revealed the gods' messages on Earth. A pilgrim – like Pelias – visited an oracle and asked a question. When the oracle spoke, the pilgrim believed it was an answer from a god.

Pelias

When Pelias was a baby, a horse had kicked him on the face. He was left with a purple mark on his cheek. This mark was known as a 'pelion', and he was named Pelias after it.

Raised by a centaur

A mother's duty is to protect her child from harm, and that is what Alcimede did. She pretended her baby was already dead, but really he was only sleeping. When Pelias came to kill Jason, he saw Alcimede and other women standing over the baby's still body. They were crying, beating their chests and pulling their hair. This was how women mourned loved ones who had died. Pelias was fooled. He let Alcimede take Jason from Iolcus, to bury the boy's body outside the town, as was the custom.

Alcimede took Jason to Mount Pelion, the tallest mountain in Thessaly, and left him in the care of Chiron the centaur. Chiron was not like other centaurs. His front legs were like those of a human, not those of a horse. Chiron was wise and kind. He raised Jason, feeding him on meat from hares and teaching him all he knew. He taught him medicine, and this knowledge gave Jason a name by which some know him – 'Jason the Healer'.

Centaurs

In the forests and mountains of northern Greece lived the centaurs. They were wild and uncontrollable flesh-eating monsters, part horse, part human. They liked the taste of alcohol, which sent them into a drunken rage. Centaurs fought mortals with tree stumps and boulders.

Now, was it three eyes of newt or two?

Are you sure this is how to make medicine?

Ask the storyteller

Did Chiron tell Jason what Pelias had done?

When he was old enough to understand, Chiron told Jason he was the son of Aeson, and that Pelias had stolen the throne of Iolcus. From then on, Jason was determined to remove Pelias from power and punish him.

13

Jason sets off to Iolcus

There came a time when Jason knew he must leave the safety of his mountain home. He was young and strong and his heart ruled his head. He had been taught to respect those older and wiser than himself, but there was one man for whom he felt only hatred. That man was Pelias – the man who had no right to be a king. Jason longed for Pelias's downfall.

On the way to Iolcus, Jason met an ugly old woman. She was stranded on the bank of the River Anaurus, unable to cross its fast-flowing water. Passers-by refused to take pity on her. Only Jason stopped to help. As he carried her across the river, he stumbled and lost a sandal. Unknown to Jason, the crone was the goddess Hera in disguise. She too wanted Pelias punished, for he had offended her by not making sacrifices in her name. Hera would protect Jason at all times.

Jason meets Pelias

An oracle warned Pelias to beware of a one-sandalled man. One day, Pelias was sacrificing a lamb to the sea-god Poseidon. In the crowd that watched the ceremony he saw a tall youth wearing only one sandal. Remembering the oracle's words, Pelias asked his name. The youth replied that he was Jason, son of Aeson.

I've lost my sandal!

Did Jason know he was talking to Pelias?

At first, Jason did not know the name of the man on the beach. Sensing this, Pelias had time to plan how to rid himself of Jason.

15

Jason is sent on a mission

Pelias thought he knew the perfect way to get rid of Jason. He asked Jason what he would do if an oracle had given him a prophecy about a dangerous stranger. Of course, Pelias was really thinking of the oracle's warning to himself. It was a trap, which Jason did not see, for he still had no idea that the man was Pelias.

Jason thought for a while, then gave his answer. He told Pelias he would send the stranger to fetch the Golden Fleece from Colchis. But the words Jason spoke were not his! The goddess Hera had put them into his mouth, as part of her plan to punish Pelias.

Only then did Pelias reveal who he was. The young man was furious and said he had come to take back the throne of Iolcus. Crafty Pelias said he could have it – in exchange for the Golden Fleece. It would be a dangerous mission for a mortal and Pelias expected Jason to die.

Fetch me the Golden Fleece!

The Golden Fleece

The Golden Fleece was the shimmering, golden skin of the talking ram Chrysomallus. This winged creature had rescued two children and flown them to Colchis, where it was sacrificed in thanks to the gods. Its fleece was hung from a tree, guarded by a serpent that never slept.

Jason will work for me, and I will protect him!

Oh Hera! What have I said?

Ask the storyteller

Where was Colchis?

Colchis was far away from Greece, at the eastern end of the Black Sea, which the Greeks called the Euxine Sea. It was in a remote area surrounded by mountains.

The Argonauts are assembled

Showing no fear, Jason accepted the challenge that Pelias had put to him. To cross the sea to Colchis, Jason needed a marvellous ship. He asked a craftsman called Argus to build one with timber from the forests of Mount Pelion, Jason's childhood home. The vessel was to be fitted out with oars for a crew of fifty men.

Skilled though he was, Argus could not complete the task alone. The goddess Athena came to his aid. She gave the ship a figurehead cut from an oak tree sacred to the great god Zeus. The figurehead had the power of speech and would guide Jason on his mission.

The ship was named *Argo*, in honour of Argus. It was a good name, for it meant 'swift'. Jason called for a crew and fifty men volunteered to sail with him. They are the heroes of this story, and are known as the Argonauts – the men who sailed in the *Argo*. At dawn, the *Argo* headed east for Colchis.

Women of Lemnos

The *Argo* stopped first at the island of Lemnos. Only women lived there, as they had killed their menfolk and taken their weapons. Some Argonauts fell in love with the women and wanted to stay with them, until Heracles, one of the Argonauts, called them back to the ship.

Were the omens good for Jason?

One of the Argonauts was Idmon, a soothsayer. He told Jason the voyage would end well, but that he, Idmon, would not live. Despite predicting his own death, Idmon still joined the mission.

Welcome, fellow Argonaut!

19

Jason kills King Cyzicus

The *Argo* continued her voyage across the blue Aegean Sea, sailed through the Hellespont – the narrow strait that separates Europe from Asia – and entered the Sea of Marmara. She sailed to the city of Cyzicus, where the Argonauts were warmly welcomed. King Cyzicus invited the men to join him at his wedding feast – but a tragedy was about to befall them all.

Anxious not to outstay their welcome, the Argonauts, their bellies full of food and wine, set sail in good spirits, sure they would soon reach Colchis. Barely had they rowed the *Argo* out of sight of Cyzicus when a storm at night blew the ship back to the land. Thinking the Argonauts were pirates, soldiers from Cyzicus attacked them in the darkness. Men who had shared food together as friends fought as enemies. In the confusion Jason drove his spear through King Cyzicus.

Heracles is lost

After the storm, the *Argo* sailed on. Heracles, the strongest Argonaut, challenged the others to a rowing contest. One by one the exhausted men dropped out, until Jason fainted and Heracles broke his oar. The ship came to rest on the banks of a river, and Heracles went in search of a tree from which to make a new oar. Next morning, Jason sailed on without Heracles – this hero took no further part in the quest for the Golden Fleece.

Ask the storyteller

What happened to Heracles?

Heracles, the greatest of all Greek heroes, went on to have his own adventures. He was set a series of tasks, which became known as the Twelve Labours of Heracles. His first labour was to kill the Nemean lion, which he did with his bare hands.

The blind man and the Harpies

The *Argo* arrived at Salmydessus. This was near the Bosporus, the channel that joins the Sea of Marmara to the Black Sea. Here lived Phineus, a king with the gift of second sight – he could see the future. But the gods could take gifts as well as give them. They took Phineus's eyes, plunging him into darkness. From then on, he could see the future, but not the present. This was not all. He was plagued by two Harpies, who stole food from his table and left him forever hungry.

Jason asked Phineus what he must do to win the Golden Fleece. Phineus promised to help on condition that Jason rid him of the Harpies. A feast was laid, and the Argonauts waited for the demons to arrive. When they did, the winged Argonauts Calais and Zetes flew at them with swords and the Harpies fled. Free from the monsters, Phineus could eat in peace. In return, he warned Jason about a danger that lay ahead.

Body-snatching Harpies

The Harpies, whose name means 'snatchers', were the winged women Aello ('Storm') and Ocypete ('Swift Flier'). They swooped down to snatch children and carry them off, never to be seen again.

Yikes! No free meal for us today!

WHAA! Get out of here!

Ask the storyteller

Where did the Harpies go?

Calais and Zetes caught up with the Harpies at the Strophades Islands (the Islands of Return). After agreeing to leave Phineus alone, they flew off to start a new life on the island of Crete.

23

At the Clashing Rocks

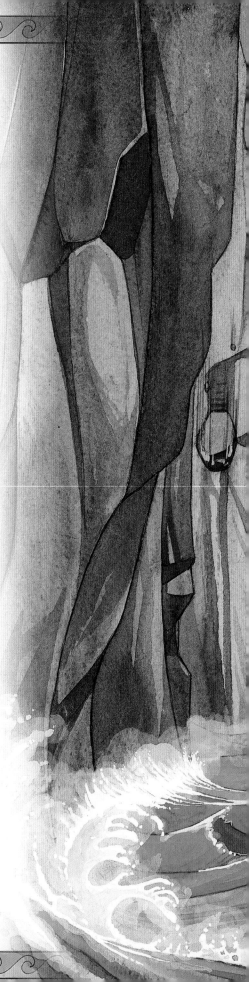

The danger that Phineus told Jason about stood in wait at the approach to the Bosporus sea channel. Here were the Symplegades – two towers of rock that guarded the narrow strait like soldiers on sentry duty. Like sentries, they challenged all who tried to pass between them, moving in until the unfortunate ship was crushed to splinters.

Jason had no choice. If he wanted to sail across the Black Sea and on to Colchis, he had to find a way past the Clashing Rocks. Phineus had told him what to do. Jason released a dove, and as it flew between the rocks the mighty towers shook and crashed together, nipping only a feather from the bird's tail. And just as Phineus had predicted, the rocks then moved back to their waiting positions, giving the *Argo* the chance to slip through the strait unharmed.

Orpheus, the singing poet

As the *Argo* passed safely through the Bosporus, Orpheus sang and played his lyre to calm the other Argonauts. His singing was so sweet it could even tame wild beasts.

Phew! That was close!

Ask the storyteller

Do the rocks still crush ships?

Not any more. Their ship-crushing days ended when they failed to trap the *Argo*. From that day to this, they have never moved again and sailors are no longer afraid of them.

25

Jason reaches Colchis

At the far end of the Black Sea, Jason and the Argonauts reached Colchis. All thoughts turned towards taking the Golden Fleece from Aeetes, the ruthless king who owned it. Aeetes promised the Fleece to Jason on condition he completed three tasks: plough a field with fire-breathing bulls; sow the field with teeth from the dragon of Cadmus; kill the skeleton warriors that grew from the teeth and burst through the soil.

Unknown to Aeetes, the goddess Hera had made Medea, his daughter, fall in love with Jason. It was part of Hera's plan to destroy Pelias. Medea gave Jason a potion that made him invincible for a day – and this was how he completed the tasks set by Aeetes. In return for her help, Jason promised to marry Medea, as long as she returned to Greece with him.

The dragon of Cadmus

This monster, whose eyes flashed fire and whose body was filled with poison, had been slain by the hero Cadmus. Its teeth were pulled out and shared between him and King Aeetes of Colchis. When they were sown in the ground, armed men came forth.

Ask the storyteller

How did Jason kill the skeleton warriors?

Medea told Jason he must throw a boulder amongst them, causing the warriors to think they were being attacked by each other. As they fought themselves, Jason walked among them and killed them one by one.

27

Jason takes the Golden Fleece

Did you really think King Aeetes would hand over the Golden Fleece? Aeetes never expected Jason to complete the tasks he'd set him, but neither did he imagine his daughter would work against him! Aeetes wanted the golden treasure to stay in Colchis, guarded by the sleepless serpent whose scaly body coiled itself around the oak tree in which the Fleece hung.

Once again, Medea, whose name means both 'cunning' and 'knowing', helped Jason. At night, she led him to the sacred grove of the Golden Fleece. Even in the darkness its wool sparkled. Medea used her knowledge to cast a spell over the Fleece's fork-tongued guardian, charming it until it was in her power. Then, as she placed magic drops into its eyes, the great snake slumped to the ground and slept. Quickly, Jason took the Fleece and returned to the *Argo* with Medea.

Sleep, serpent, sleep.

Aeetes gives chase

As the new day dawned, King Aeetes discovered he had lost not one but his two most precious treasures in life – the Golden Fleece and his daughter. He sent a fleet of fast ships to chase after the *Argo*, but even he could not imagine what cunning Medea would do next.

He's got the Golden Fleece!

ZZZZZZ

Ask the storyteller

What did Medea do next?

As Medea was under the control of Hera, the goddess made her do a wicked thing. Medea had taken her brother Apsyrtus hostage. She killed him, chopped up his body and threw the pieces into the sea. When her father's ships stopped to collect the pieces, the *Argo* sailed away.

29

Song of the Sirens

The voyage home was as difficult as the journey to Colchis had been. Blown far off course, the *Argo* sailed to the coast of Italy, until she came to the island of Anthemoessa, whose name means 'flowery'. On this island lived three Sirens – demons of the sea with wings and bodies of birds and heads of women. Their beautiful singing was a sound all sailors feared, as it enchanted men and lured their ships onto the rocks.

This was a fate the *Argo* avoided. Jason commanded Orpheus to sing for the Argonauts and as they listened to their companion's sweet voice they rowed the ship to safety. Only one sailor, Butes, heard the song of the Sirens. He jumped into the water and swam to them.

Ask the storyteller

Did Jason marry Medea?

Yes, he did. They were married on the island of Corfu, where they spent their wedding night in a cave, sleeping on the Golden Fleece.

Washed ashore

From Corfu, a tidal wave swept the *Argo* south to the deserts of north Africa. For nine days the Argonauts carried their ship overland, until they reached the Mediterranean Sea and sailed for home once more.

Sing louder, Orpheus!

Let my song fill your ears – it will take away your fears.

Talos the giant

I'm leaking to death!

The Argonauts reached the island of Crete. Here they met Talos, a giant with a bronze body. He pelted them with rocks, until Medea cast a spell to make him pull a stopper from his ankle. Out poured his liquid metal 'blood' and his life drained away.

The end of the story

Jason, Medea and the Argonauts finally reached Iolcus. King Pelias never dreamed that Jason would return, convinced that the mission to take the Golden Fleece was an impossible one. While Jason had been away, Pelias had killed Aeson and Alcimede, Jason's parents. Now the time had come for this evil man, stealer of the throne of Iolcus, destroyer of the royal family, to die – but not by the hand of Jason.

For one last time, Medea used her cunning. But, as before, it was the goddess Hera who willed her on, in order to punish Pelias. Medea said she could make new life from old. She killed an old ram and put its pieces into a cooking pot, from which emerged, as if by magic, a young lamb. Pelias wanted to be young again, so he let his three daughters kill him, chop up his body and boil the pieces in the cauldron. Of course, it was all a trick. Pelias was dead.

Jason flees

Jason never became king of Iolcus. He was forced to flee by Acastus, son of Pelias, who became the new king. Jason and Medea went to Corinth, where they settled and had a family.

Happily ever after?

Medea and Jason fell out and she went away. Jason, who was lonely, visited the *Argo* to remember the good times. It was a wreck, and one day its figurehead fell and killed him.

Father!

Ask the storyteller

What happened to the Golden Fleece?

Before he settled in Corinth, Jason took the Golden Fleece to the temple of Zeus at Orchomenus, a city in eastern Greece, and that was where he left it.

The Twelve Labours of Heracles

Meet the heroes

Heracles
The son of Zeus and Alcmene has superhuman strength. But how will he cope with these twelve tough tests?

Artemis
Daughter of Zeus, twin sister of Apollo, Artemis is the goddess of hunting and of the night. Don't get on the wrong side of her!

Eurystheus
The rich and cowardly king of Mycenae thinks he can get the better of our mighty hero. What do you think?

Atlas
Atlas is one of the giants who were defeated by Zeus and the other gods of Mount Olympus. His task is to hold up the sky.

Iolaus
Meet Heracles's nephew. He may not be as strong as Heracles, but he's bright – and sometimes brain is better than brawn.

Hippolyte
She is the queen of the Amazons, a fearsome tribe of female warriors, expert at hunting and archery.

Introduction

Gather round and hear my story. I will tell you all of the greatest hero the world has ever seen. Of whom am I speaking? Why, Heracles of course! Storytellers of old say that he was the son of a beautiful woman called Alcmene, and the king of the Gods, Zeus. But just because his father was a god, it didn't mean that Heracles had an easy life. Zeus's wife, Hera, made sure of that. She was angry that Zeus had fathered a child with a mortal woman and she despised Heracles. In revenge, she cast a spell on him, which made him kill his wife and children. When Heracles realised the terrible crime he had committed, he asked the famous oracle at Delphi how he could pay for his dreadful crime. He was told to travel to the kingdom of Mycenae and visit King Eurystheus. Only by obeying the king's every command would Heracles ever be forgiven for killing his family.

I am the storyteller – lend me your ears!

The Nemean Lion

King Eurystheus was pleased to have a new servant to perform his every wish. For fun, he decided to set Heracles 12 impossible labours, or tasks, and looked forward to seeing the brave young man fail. First of these was to kill a ferocious lion in the land of Nemea. This fearsome creature had been devouring local people and terrorising the land. It lived in a deep cave with two entrances, so that it always had an escape route. Its skin was so thick that no sword could pierce it. Heracles soon found out that arrows were useless as well. He fired a whole quiver-full, but they all bounced off harmlessly. So the hero changed his tactics. Blocking off one of the entrances to the lion's den with a huge boulder, Heracles chased the beast inside. In this way he cornered the lion and wrestled it with his bare hands. After a great contest, Heracles strangled the savage beast.

Eurystheus and his jar

When Heracles returned to Eurystheus's kingdom with the dead lion, the king was so terrified that he hid in a *pithos*, a large jar made for storing food.

Ask the storyteller

What happened to the lion?

Not wanting to waste his prize, Heracles skinned the dead lion and wore its pelt over his body.

37

The Hydra of Lerna

King Eurystheus was embarrassed when he eventually emerged from his jar. He decided to set Heracles an even more difficult second task – to kill the Hydra. You will have to stretch your minds to imagine this terrible monster. It had the body of a dragon and nine heads, each with a ravenous mouth lined with sharp teeth. To find the Hydra, Heracles had to travel to the land of Lerna, and the swamp in which it lived.

Facing one enemy was hard enough, but this was like facing nine at the same time. Heracles first tried to chop off the Hydra's heads, but each time he did so, two more grew to replace it. With his enemy multiplying, Heracles came up with a solution. Every time he cut through one of the Hydra's necks, his companion Iolaus would hold a lighted torch to the wound to stop a new head appearing. In this way the Hydra was finally vanquished.

The poisoned arrows

As the Hydra lay dead, Heracles dipped his arrow tips in the creature's blood, which made them deadly poisonous.

Ask the storyteller

Who was Iolaus?

Iolaus was the son of Heracles's half-brother Iphicles, and as well as helping Heracles with his Labours, he was also said to drive Heracles's chariot for him.

39

The Ceryneian Deer

Seeing that Heracles had no problems killing creatures, King Eurystheus next sent the hero to capture a magical deer in the land of Ceryneia. This creature was sacred to the goddess Artemis, so it would be a great crime if Heracles were to kill it. The animal had golden antlers and hooves of bronze and people say it could run as fast as the wind. Whether this is quite true or not, Heracles chased the deer for a whole year without stopping, before finally immobilising it with an arrow in the land of Arcadia. He fired at its front legs, to be sure not to kill it. Then, hoisting the beautiful creature on to his broad shoulders, he carried his catch back to King Eurystheus. The king demanded that Heracles dedicate it to the goddess Artemis at her temple.

A squabble with a god

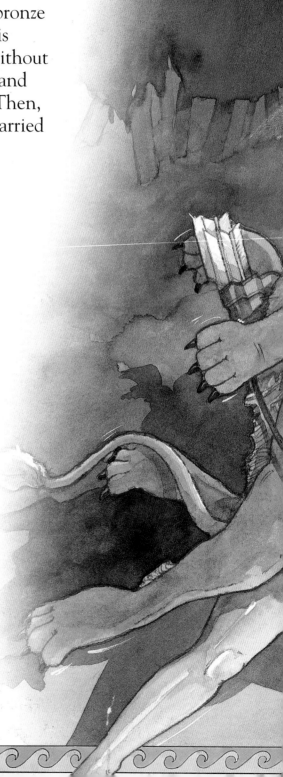

When Heracles was carrying the deer back to Eurystheus, he met the god Apollo on the way. Apollo tried to take the creature from Heracles, saying that Heracles was trying to kill the sacred animal. However, Heracles managed to explain his actions and Apollo let him go on his way.

Ask the storyteller

Who was the goddess Artemis?

Artemis was goddess of the Moon and hunting. She roamed the forest with a band of loyal followers – all of them female.

I hope this doesn't kill it.

The Erymanthian Boar

As his fourth labour, King Eurystheus sent Heracles to capture a ferocious boar, a kind of wild pig, which lived on Mount Erymanthus. This huge creature had long tusks coming from its mouth and a terrible temper. For years it had terrorised the local farmers, destroying their crops and goring them to death.

Heracles forced the animal into the open by shouting threats and throwing his spear, eventually chasing it to the very top of the mountain, where deep snow lay. The boar, now exhausted after the long chase, became stuck in a large snowdrift and Heracles managed to snare it in a net. He then dragged it all the way back to Mycenae. He didn't get as far as King Eurystheus's palace, however. He just dropped the trussed-up boar in the marketplace of the city and went to join another hero, Jason, on his ship, the *Argo*.

A battle with the centaurs

On his way to do battle with the boar, Heracles stopped for a drink with a famous centaur called Pholus. Other centaurs were jealous and tried to kill Heracles, but he drove them off with logs from the fire.

Come on, you fat pig!

Ask the storyteller

What happened to Pholus?

While Heracles was dealing with the angry centaurs, Pholus tried to pick up the hero's bow and arrows to help. Unfortunately, one of the poisoned arrows fell on his foot and killed him.

The Stables of King Augeas

Well, Heracles had proved that he was both brave and strong, but his next task would require his wits as well. He had to clean out the stables of the King of Elis, called Augeas. This king had more cattle than anyone else in Greece, including goats, sheep, horses and cows. They were all kept together in a stable which had not been cleaned for 30 years. You can imagine the mess! And Heracles was told to complete the task in a single day!

He tackled the problem using his brain more than his brawn. He knocked two holes in opposite ends of the stables. Then, with the help of Iolaus, he diverted two nearby rivers, Alpheus and Peneus, so that they flowed through the first hole and washed all the mess out through the second. So Heracles was successful without so much as dirtying his hands.

Augeas breaks the deal

King Augeas had promised that if Heracles was successful, he could keep one tenth of the cattle for himself. However, when Heracles came to claim his payment, the king refused to give him anything and said that he had never made such a bargain.

45

The Stymphalian Birds

Heracles's sixth Labour took him to northern Greece and the land of Stymphalus. Here, above a marsh, lived a flock of birds you'd never want to come across. They were giant winged creatures, with bronze beaks and razor-sharp talons. Not surprisingly, they were sacred to the god of war and weapons, Ares, and a terror to the people who farmed in the area. When Heracles arrived he could not get close to them, because he feared treading in the marsh and drowning. Nor could he kill them straightaway with his arrows, because they cowered in the tall trees above, or the long marsh grasses below. With a little help from the gods he found the answer. Using a magical rattle, called a *krotala*, he scared the birds out of their hiding place. Then, as they flew away, he quickly shot them down one by one. The sky was full of feathers and the curse of Stymphalus was finally lifted.

Man-eaters...

...or nuisances?

Some stories say that the birds were flesh-eaters, which carried off children and animals, while others say that they were just a menace, poisoning crops with their droppings. Either way, the people who lived nearby were happy to be rid of them.

PLOP

Ask the storyteller

Where did Heracles get the rattle from?

The *krotala* were made by Hephaestus, the god of blacksmiths, who was rumoured to be very ugly. He gave them to the goddess Athena, who passed them on to Heracles.

The Cretan Bull

Heracles's seventh labour took him to the island of Crete to capture a famous bull which lived there. The animal was sacred to the god Poseidon and had an interesting history. A man called Minos had wanted to prove to the people of Crete that he was the rightful king, so he asked the gods to send him a miracle that would convince the citizens. Poseidon heard the prayer and made the bull appear out of the sea, much to the astonishment of the Cretans. However, when Minos was supposed to sacrifice the beautiful animal he refused, because he wanted to keep it for himself. His fate is another story. What we need to know is that Heracles wrestled the bull until he tired it out, then set off to show it to King Eurystheus.

The Minotaur

To punish King Minos for not sacrificing the bull, Poseidon made his wife fall in love with it. To Minos's shame, his wife Pasiphae gave birth to a child called the Minotaur, which was half-man, half-bull, and ate human flesh! Minos imprisoned this creature in a maze called the Labyrinth, where it was eventually killed by another hero, Theseus.

49

The Horses of King Diomedes

By now, Eurystheus was becoming tired of Heracles's successes. He sent him on a particularly dangerous mission, hoping if he returned at least a few limbs would be missing. So Heracles travelled over the sea to Thrace, where a king named Diomedes ruled over a tribe called the Bistones. Heracles's orders were to capture the four mares which pulled Diomedes's chariot. The problem was that the horses liked the taste of human flesh and would devour anyone who came near them. People say King Diomedes kept them under control by feeding them his unsuspecting guests!

With the help of his friend Abderus, Heracles overcame the grooms who looked after the savage beasts and drove them down to the sea where his boat awaited. However, Diomedes and the Bistones gave chase and Heracles had to fight them off.

Dragged to death

While Heracles dealt with the Bistones, he put his friend Abderus in charge of the mares. Unfortunately they were too powerful for him to handle and he was pulled along the ground until he died.

Ask the storyteller

What happened to King Diomedes?

He came to a sticky end. Heracles fed the former master to his hungry horses. This magically made them tame and easy to control.

It'll be feeding time soon, Diomedes!

The Girdle of Hippolyte

Heracles's next task was of a slightly different kind. To the east of the Aegean Sea lived a band of fierce women called the Amazons. Even most men thought twice about facing them in battle. King Eurystheus ordered Heracles to fetch the girdle, a type of belt, worn by the Queen of the Amazons, Hippolyte. This was a belt used to hold her sword and spear and she would not give it up without a fight. So once again Heracles set sail with a small band of men, determined to fulfil the task.

When Heracles first met Hippolyte she fell in love with him and offered him the girdle of her own free will. However, Heracles's old enemy, the goddess Hera, stirred up hatred against him amongst the other Amazons. In the end, he and his men had to fight a bloody battle against them. Although he didn't want to, Heracles ended up killing Hippolyte with a stray arrow.

Warrior women

The Amazons hated men. They killed almost all of their male children at birth and made the rest slaves. The girls were raised to be soldiers. Amazon women were especially famous for their prowess on horseback.

Why did Eurystheus want the girdle?

He didn't want it for himself. The king's daughter, Admete, had asked for the girdle as a gift. Eurystheus thought he may as well use Heracles to get it.

You'll wish you never messed with this woman!

53

The Cattle of Geryon

Heracles's next labour took him right across to the other side of the known world, to the land of Eurythia. His task was to steal the cattle of Geryon. These were strong, magical beasts, which grazed in the pastures there. Geryon was a giant with three heads, three bodies and six legs and arms, who loved his animals dearly. Some say he was the strongest person who ever lived. His herd was guarded by a shepherd called Eurytion and a snarling, two-headed dog called Orthrus. Heracles first killed these two with his club, before turning to the problem of Geryon himself. It was a very difficult fight, because the deformed giant could look in all directions at the same time. However, Heracles came up with a solution and killed him with a single arrow that pierced all three bodies through their one heart.

The Pillars of Heracles

To make his way to Eurythia, Heracles had to part the lands we now know as Africa and Europe. He built two huge pillars on either side of the strait to keep it open for his return journey.

Ask the storyteller

How did Heracles take the cattle back?

As a reward for his hard work, the Sun god, Helios, gave Heracles a great golden bowl in which to cross the sea. It was a rough ride, but he got home in the end.

The Golden Apples of the Hesperides

For Heracles's eleventh labour, he had to fetch the golden apples from a sacred garden at the ends of the Earth. The orchard was tended by the Hesperides, nymphs who were daughters of the Titan Atlas. It was also guarded by a terrible, two-headed serpent called Ladon. Heracles had no idea how he would complete the task, but on his way there he came across some unexpected help. He found a man called Prometheus, who was being punished by the gods because he had stolen from them. Heracles freed him and in return Prometheus told the hero to seek out Atlas, who would go and get the apples for him. Heracles soon found him, but there was a problem. Atlas's job was to hold the world on his shoulders. So, while he went to fetch the apples the hero agreed to hold up the globe in the meantime.

Oh no! Not again!

Prometheus's punishment

Prometheus had stolen the gift of fire from Mount Olympus, to give to mortal men. As a punishment Zeus had chained him to a cliff, where every day a giant eagle would come down and peck out his liver. Every night the liver grew back, so Prometheus's torture was never-ending.

Keeper of the Underworld

Heracles had now been at his labours for eleven long years. His final duty was by far the most dangerous. King Eurystheus told him to descend to the Underworld, a task which few mortals had managed. And this was not all he had to do. Heracles would also have to bring back the ferocious dog, Cerberus, who guarded the dark kingdom. However, Cerberus was no ordinary dog. He had three heads, and a coat bristling with poisonous snakes.

Heracles descended into the Underworld through a cavern in a place called Taenarum. He then crossed the River Styx and visited Hades, ruler of the dead, and asked if he could take the dog away. Hades gave him permission, provided he use only his brute strength and no weapons. Heracles succeeded, but when he took the beast before Eurystheus, the king was so scared he ordered it to be returned immediately.

Rescuing an old friend

While in the Underworld, Heracles freed his friend, the hero Theseus. Theseus and his friend Pirithous had been captured trying to free Hades's queen, Persephone, whom Hades had abducted from the land of the living.

Maybe he'll rescue me as well!

Ask the storyteller

Is that the end?

With his 12 labours completed, Heracles had fulfilled his debt to Hera. He went on to become the most famous of all Greek heroes, celebrated in art and poetry for centuries to come.

The Wooden Horse of Troy

Meet the heroes

Paris
The young Trojan prince has to judge a beauty contest. In return, he is promised the love of the world's most beautiful woman...

Achilles
Achilles is the Greeks' greatest warrior, though he's not an easy person to get on with. And he's immortal – well, almost.

Helen
...and everyone agrees that the most beautiful woman is Helen. But she is already married to Menelaus – what will he say?

Hector
Paris's elder brother is the noblest and most valiant of the Trojan warriors. He is said to be protected by the god Apollo.

Agamemnon
Helen's brother-in-law, the warlike king of Mycenae, leads the Greek army against Troy to get Helen back.

Athena
The goddess Athena is furious with the Trojans because Paris thought she was less beautiful than Aphrodite.

introduction

Greetings citizens! Gather round! I am the rhapsode – the teller of stories. You may have heard of the great siege at Troy – the beautiful woman who caused the conflict, the brave warriors who fought and fell for what they believed and the trickery that finally ended it all. Lend me your ears for...

I come this day from far away
With a tale to tell that spins a spell,
Which you will hear – if you draw near –
Of times of old and heroes bold.

So gather round and hear my story
Which I will weave from ancient glory,
By joining threads from start to end –
Then you may pass it to a friend.

Now, let me check the sources...

Troy – built with the gods' help

My story begins long, long ago, in an age when immortal gods mixed with humans on Earth. The great Zeus sent his son, Apollo, and his brother, Poseidon, to work among men. It was a punishment, because they had rebelled against him. For one whole year Apollo and Poseidon worked for Laomedon, the King of Troy, building strong walls around his city. But they had not worked alone. They asked Aeacus, one of the humans, to help.

Laomedon had promised his famous immortal horses as payment for the gods' help. But he broke his promise when the work was completed. Apollo sent a plague upon Troy and Poseidon ordered a monstrous sea serpent to attack the city. Laomedon visited an oracle to seek advice and was told that he must sacrifice his daughter, Hesione, to the serpent. But he could not bear to lose her. Instead, he promised his horses to whoever killed the monster. This brave deed fell to the hero Heracles but, again, Laomedon broke his promise.

The snakes that foretold the future

When the walls of Troy were built, three snakes slithered to the top of them. The two snakes that climbed the parts built by the gods fell down dead. However, the snake that climbed the wall built by Aeacus slid into the city. Apollo said it was a sign that Troy would be taken over by the descendants of Aeacus.

Ask the storyteller

What did Heracles do?

Heracles was angry because Laomedon had not given up his horses. He left Troy, but returned many years later to kill Laomedon and his sons. Hesione successfully pleaded with Heracles to spare her brother, Podarces, who from then on was known as Priam – the new King of Troy.

Build high! Build strong!

The judgement of Paris

In time, King Priam and his wife, Hecabe, had a son called Paris. However, before the child's birth, Hecabe had a nightmare that she would give birth to a flaming torch. She thought this was a bad omen and was afraid of her new son, so she left baby Paris to die on a mountain. But he didn't. Luckily, he was found by a shepherd who raised him as his own son.

Paris grew into a fine young man who worked as a shepherd. One day, as he tended his flock, he came upon three goddesses: Hera, Athena and Aphrodite. They were arguing over a golden apple, upon which was written "For the most beautiful". They asked Zeus to decide, but he ordered Paris to be the judge. Hera offered to give him Asia and Europe if he chose her; Athena vowed to make him a great warrior; Aphrodite promised him Helen, the most beautiful woman in the world. Overcome with love for Helen, Paris gave the apple to Aphrodite.

The Apple of Strife

A goddess called Eris had thrown the apple amongst the goddesses, because they had been invited to a wedding and she had not. She knew they would argue over who was the most beautiful of them all.

Ask the storyteller

Did Paris choose wisely?

Poor Paris. He allowed himself to be tempted by the bribes of the goddesses and let his heart rule his head. His love for Helen was strong, but in choosing her his fate was sealed, as was that of the city of Troy.

I choose your gift, goddess Aphrodite.

Paris takes Helen to Troy

Many men had asked for Helen's hand in marriage. But her father Tyndareus, King of Sparta, would only let her marry on one condition – that all the men who loved her would always protect her. They agreed and swore an oath. Helen was free to choose a husband and she picked a noble called Menelaus, from the city of Mycenae.

Ten years had passed since Paris's meeting with the three goddesses. During this time Paris had returned to Troy and was accepted back into his real family. But Aphrodite had not forgotten her promise to him. She waited until Menelaus was away from Sparta, then took Paris to meet Helen. With a little help from Aphrodite, Paris led Helen to his ship at night, loaded it with treasure, then sailed away back to Troy.

When Menelaus discovered what had happened, he was furious.

A last resort

At first, Menelaus tried to get Helen back by peaceful means. He went to Troy and pleaded for his wife's safe return, but all his demands were rejected. From then on, he knew that the only way to win Helen's freedom was by defeating the Trojans in war.

Ask the storyteller

Why did Helen go with Paris?

Aphrodite cast a powerful spell over Helen, making her fall in love with Paris. Some say the goddess made Paris look like Menelaus, tricking Helen into believing she was with her husband.

The fleet sails to Troy

Menelaus visited his brother, Agamemnon, King of Mycenae, to ask for help. Agamemnon called on all the men who had sworn to protect Helen. In this way the Greeks assembled an army, with Agamemnon as their leader.

Agamemnon gathered one thousand ships at the port of Aulis, ready to take the Greek army across the sea to Troy. But a prophet, Calchas, said the fleet must not sail until Achilles had joined them, because Troy could only be conquered with the hero's help. Calchas, who was skilled in reading signs sent by the gods, saw a snake which ate nine sparrows and then turned itself into stone. He said this omen meant that Troy would only be captured after ten years of war. Calchas's next prophecy was grim: Agamemnon must sacrifice his own daughter, Iphigeneia, to please the gods. So, Agamemnon called the girl to him, pretending she was to be married to Achilles. But this was just a trick – she was sacrificed on an altar. After the sacrifice the wind blew strong and the fleet set sail to Troy.

Philoctetes is abandoned

On the way to Troy the Greeks landed at the island of Tenedos. There, the archer Philoctetes was bitten on the foot by a snake. He was in agony and his wound was so bad that the Greeks left him there against his will and sailed away without him.

Ask the storyteller

Why did the Greeks want Achilles to fight with them?

Everyone knew that Achilles was the strongest hero of all, so it was vital that he joined the army. As a baby his mother had dipped him in the waters of the River Styx to make him invulnerable – so no harm could come to him. However, his heel had not touched the water and this was his weak point.

The siege of Troy

When the army came ashore, the citizens and soldiers of Troy looked down on the Greeks from the strong walls the gods had helped build. Agamemnon and his men made camp outside the city and a siege began, which would last for ten long years.

In the tenth year, Agamemnon captured a girl called Chryseis and would not release her. Unfortunately, her father was one of Apollo's priests. This angered the god. He sent a plague upon the Greek army, which made them fear for their lives.

Achilles called a meeting and it was decreed that Agamemnon should return Chryseis. Agamemnon did this, but, to make up for his loss, stole Achilles's favourite slave-girl, Briseis. This caused a great argument between the two men. In anger, Achilles refused to have anything else to do with the fight against the Trojans. This was a terrible blow for Agamemnon, since he remembered Calchas's prophecy that Troy could not be conquered without Achilles.

How Odysseus escaped death

There was a prophecy which said that the first Greek who set foot on Trojan soil would be the first to die in battle. Knowing this, Odysseus, who was first to leave the ships, threw his shield to the ground and stood on it. Next out was Protesilaus. He followed Odysseus but was the first to tread on the land. The prophecy was fulfilled and he was the first to be killed.

Ask the storyteller

Did the Greeks give peace a chance?

Even after the conflict had started, the Greeks sent ambassadors who asked for Helen and the stolen treasure to be returned. But the Trojans would not listen. Instead, they threw insults and rubbish down on the Greeks from the safety of the city walls.

Let battle commence!

Even though the plague had claimed the lives of many of the Greeks, and Achilles was no longer fighting alongside him, Agamemnon chose to fight on. It was a bad choice to make. Unknown to him, Achilles, who was sulking, had called on the gods to punish Agamemnon – and all because he had freed Briseis, his slave-girl. The gods answered Achilles's call for help, and for a time they let the Trojans defeat the Greeks in one struggle after another. It looked as though the Trojans would win the war and send the Greeks back across the sea empty-handed. Many things happened in the tenth year of the Trojan War...

A lucky escape!

A truce was called, so that Paris and Menelaus could fight a duel. The winner would take Helen and the war would end. However, when Menelaus was about to kill Paris, the goddess Aphrodite, who was on Paris's side, made him vanish.

Athena interferes

The goddess Athena did not want the war to stop. She disguised herself as a Trojan and persuaded an archer to fire an arrow from the walls of Troy. His arrow struck Menelaus and wounded him. Firing an arrow broke the truce, and so the war started again.

Assassination!

The heroes Odysseus and Diomedes killed Rhesus, King of the Thracians, who was fighting on the side of the Trojans. They stole his pure white horses, which shone as bright as sunbeams, were as fast as the wind and could become invisible.

Thersites the coward

Thersites, the ugliest of the Greeks, demanded that Agamemnon abandon the war so that the men could return home safely to Greece. No one took any notice of Thersites. Odysseus beat him with his staff until he apologised for speaking out.

An even fight

Ajax, a mighty Greek, fought a duel with Hector, the bravest of the Trojans. The fight lasted all day, with neither man winning. When night fell, they exchanged gifts, and parted as equals.

Ask the storyteller
Where was Achilles while all this was happening?

Because of his argument with Agamemnon, Achilles, the bravest of all the Greeks, did not take part in the fighting. Instead, he stayed inside his tent with his friend Patroclus.

The fleet in flames

With help from the gods, Hector broke through the Greeks' defences on the beach and set their ships on fire. For as long as Achilles stayed out of the fighting, the gods helped the Trojans beat the Greeks.

Achilles kills Hector

With the war going against them, the Greeks feared the gods had deserted them – which they had! Their only hope of victory rested with Achilles. Agamemnon called on the hero to return to the war, promising to give Briseis back. He offered him treasure. He promised him 20 of the most beautiful women of Troy. He even offered the hand of one of his own daughters in marriage. But Achilles, still sulking, refused all Agamemnon's gifts.

When Hector the Trojan burned the Greeks' ships, Achilles's friend Patroclus begged to return to the fight. Achilles lent his own armour to Patroclus, to fool the Trojans into thinking it was actually Achilles who was fighting. But Hector was far stronger than Patroclus and soon killed him. Overcome with grief at the death of his friend, Achilles told Agamemnon their quarrel was over and that he would return to the war.

Achilles pursued Hector around the walls of Troy. Finally they fought and Achilles killed his enemy with a spear through his throat. He tied Hector's lifeless body to his chariot and dragged it around Troy, so the Trojans would see that their greatest warrior was dead.

The death of Patroclus

After Hector had killed Patroclus, he stripped Achilles's armour from his dead body and wore it as his own. Achilles grieved for Patroclus and arranged a grand funeral for him, at which 12 Trojan prisoners were sacrificed to the gods. When Achilles killed Hector, he took his armour back.

Ask the storyteller

What happened to Hector's body?

Achilles dragged Hector's body behind his chariot for many days. Dogs and birds picked at it. Only when Priam, the King of Troy, paid a ransom was the body returned to his people. Hector was given a hero's funeral and there was a truce that lasted 12 days.

The Greeks will be victorious!

The death of Achilles

Now that Achilles was back fighting, the war at last turned in favour of the Greeks. They began to defeat their Trojan enemy. Penthesilea, queen of the Amazons, came to fight with the Trojans. Although she fought bravely, Penthesilea was no match for Achilles and he cut her down. On seeing Achilles's admiration for the dead queen, Thersites mocked him. It was to be the final act of this ugly wretch. Achilles turned on Thersites and killed him, too.

But even Achilles's days were numbered. Although everyone believed he couldn't be harmed, he did have a weak spot. When Achilles and Paris met in combat, Apollo guided the Trojan's arrow towards the one part of Achilles's body left unprotected by the waters of the River Styx. The arrow struck Achilles in the heel and his life drained away. The hero of the Greeks was dead. Mighty Ajax carried Achilles's body to the Greeks' camp, where he was mourned for 17 days. His body was then burned on a funeral pyre and his ashes mixed with those of his friend, Patroclus.

Paris is killed

Philoctetes, abandoned on the island of Tenedos, was keeper of the bow and arrows of Heracles. He entered the war when Odysseus stole his weapons. He followed Odysseus, who led him to Troy. With a poisoned arrow, shot from the bow of Heracles, Philoctetes killed Paris.

My...life... is...over...

Ask the storyteller

What happened to Ajax?

A contest was held to see who should be given Achilles's armour. Ajax expected to win, but he lost out to Odysseus. In a moment of despair and madness, he killed the sheep which the Greeks kept for food. Afraid of being mocked, he put his sword in the ground, fell on it and killed himself.

The Wooden Horse of Troy

It so happened the Greeks had captured a Trojan prophet who could see into the future. He said the Greeks must do three things if they were to capture Troy: bring Philoctetes to fight with them (they did and he killed Paris); the son of Achilles must fight in the war (he did); a sacred statue must be stolen from the Trojans (it was). So much for the Trojan's prediction – the siege continued.

It was the goddess Athena who told the Greeks what to do. On her instructions they built a wooden horse which soldiers could hide inside. These words were written on the outside of the horse: "For their return home, the Greeks dedicate this as thanks to Athena". The horse was dragged to Troy, and left outside its gates. Then, the Greek army boarded its ships and sailed away, pretending they had abandoned the war. Only one man called Sinon stayed behind.

Next morning, the Trojans could not believe their luck – the Greeks had gone. Sinon, who had let them capture him, told them that the horse was a gift to Athena. He said that the horse was too big for the Trojans to take inside their city. This made the Trojans more eager to bring it within the walls of Troy and prove the Greeks wrong.

Twelve brave men

No-one knows how many men were hidden inside the wooden horse. The story is so old that the number is long forgotten. Some say there were 23 or 30, others say 50, 100 or even 3,000. I believe there were just twelve.

Ask the storyteller

Was everyone fooled by the Greeks' trickery?

Although some Trojans were suspicious about the Greeks' 'gift', only one man spoke out. He was a priest called Laocoon. However, the goddess Athena sent two giant sea-serpents, which killed both Laocoon and his two sons. The people thought that this was punishment for refusing the gift.

Come on, Sinon, tell us the truth.

The horse will fit if you say so...

The fall of Troy

The only way the horse could be brought into Troy was by taking down part of the city wall (the part built by Aeacus). With this done, it was dragged through the gap. The Trojans finally celebrated because they thought victory was theirs.

Inside the wooden horse, the Greek soldiers stayed still and quiet. They waited until nightfall when the Trojans were asleep, then crept from their hiding place and opened the gates to the city. From high up on the walls of Troy, Helen – the woman over whom the war had been fought – lit a torch. Its flame was seen from far away by the Greek army. This was their signal that Troy was open to attack.

The Greeks destroyed the city, ransacked its temples and looted its treasures. Priam, the King of Troy, was killed. Hecabe, his wife, and Cassandra, his daughter, were taken prisoner. The baby son of Hector, the Trojans' fallen warrior, was thrown from the city walls and Hector's wife became a captive of the victorious Greeks.

Why Helen helped the Greeks

Helen had lived in Troy for many years. She had become the wife of Paris, the Trojan who had tricked her into leaving Sparta. In all this time she had wished to return to Greece. Odysseus told her that if she betrayed the Trojans her wish would come true.

Ask the storyteller

What happened to Helen?

Let us not forget that the Trojan War started because the Trojans had taken Helen, the most beautiful woman in the world, away from Menelaus, her husband. But this story has a happy ending. With the fall of Troy, Helen was reunited with Menelaus.

The return of the heroes

After ten years of war the heroes hoped to be home in a few days, but this was not to be. The gods were angry with the Greeks. They had not wanted Troy – a city they had helped build – to be so completely destroyed. They regarded the destruction of its temples as an act of sacrilege.

So, in punishment, the gods sent a great storm to batter the returning Greek fleet. Many ships were sunk, leaving only a few to reach safety. One was Agamemnon's ship, which was protected by the goddess Hera. Though he returned to his palace, a surprise awaited him. While he had been away his wife, Clytemnestra, had fallen in love with another man. She no longer wanted Agamemnon, so she murdered him while he was bathing.

Athena's anger

The goddess Athena had supported the Greeks all through the war, but she was angry when they turned the city to rubble. She punished them with a storm.

Ask the storyteller

Did Helen and Menelaus live happily ever after?

After the storm it took seven long years for Menelaus and Helen to travel home. When they finally returned to Sparta, they had been away from the city for a total of seventeen years. They spent the rest of their lives there. When Menelaus was old, Zeus took him to the Elysian fields and Apollo made Helen into a goddess.

The end of the story?

And so we reach the end of our storyteller's tale. However, the end of one story is often the beginning of the next. From the ruins of Troy came forth a Trojan hero – a leader who had fought the Greeks. His name was Aeneas. He fled the city, carrying his lame father, Anchises, on his shoulders, and his young son, Ascanius, in his arms. He also took with him objects which were sacred to the gods of Troy.

Aeneas travelled far and wide looking for a place to found a new kingdom. He moved to Thrace, then to the island of Delos and then to Crete, but he was not destined to settle in any of these places. Nor was he to find any peace in Sicily, the island on which his father died. Only when he reached Italy did his fortune change. He came to the River Tiber and entered the region ruled by King Latinus. Aeneas married the king's daughter, Lavinia, and founded a city which he named Lavinium, in her honour. When his son, Ascanius, was a man, he too founded a city in Italy. Many years later, Romulus, a descendant of Aeneas, founded yet another city, called Rome – perhaps you have heard of it.

Aeneas, father of the Romans

It was predicted that one day Aeneas would eat the plate his food came on, and the place where that happened would be his new home. On the banks of the River Tiber, in Italy, Aeneas ate the thin loaf of bread he was using as a plate. It was there that he founded the city of Lavinium.

We must start again my son, far away from Troy.

Ask the storyteller

What happened to Troy?

With its royal family dead, its population killed or sold into slavery, the city of Troy was in ruins, never to be lived in again. All that is left is its distant memory, which is kept alive through stories like this one.

The Voyages of Odysseus

Meet the heroes

Odysseus
Odysseus (or Ulysses) is famous for his cunning. And he will need it as he battles his way home from the Trojan War.

Penelope
Odysseus has been away so long that most people think he's dead. But his faithful wife Penelope is sure that he'll return.

Polyphemus
This mighty cyclops – a one-eyed giant – is the son of Poseidon, god of the sea. He's big enough to make mincemeat of our hero!

Telemachus
Telemachus was only a child when his father Odysseus went to Troy. But he, too, believes that Odysseus will come back.

Circe
The beautiful but dangerous Circe is a powerful sorceress. No man has ever escaped from her enchanted palace.

Poseidon
When you're adrift on the high seas, the last thing you want is to have the sea-god Poseidon as your sworn enemy...

Introduction

Gather round and hear my story. I shall tell you about one of the greatest heroes Greece has ever known – the brave Odysseus, king of the island of Ithaca. His story began when he joined his Greek comrades to fight the city of Troy. For ten years they besieged the city until Odysseus – the most cunning of the Greeks – found a way to trick the Trojans and end the war. He and some warriors hid inside a huge wooden horse, hoping that the Trojans would drag it into the city. Foolishly, this is just what they did! At night the Greeks climbed out and opened the city gates for their comrades. Surprised by their enemies, the Trojans were defeated. Sick of war and eager to be reunited with his wife, Penelope, Odysseus and his fleet of twelve ships were at last able to go home.

From one feast to the next

Travelling back to Ithaca, Odysseus and his men first put ashore at Ismarus, a city in Thrace. They rampaged through the city, looting and killing, before hurrying back to their boats. Odysseus wisely wanted to leave before the locals could seek revenge, but his men chose to feast and then fell into a drunken sleep. They were woken by the shouts of the Cicones, neighbouring warriors who had come to avenge the deaths of their friends. There was bloody fighting, and though the Greeks escaped to their ships, 72 men were killed.

Grieving for their dead comrades, the men sailed onward to the land of the Lotus-Eaters. There Odysseus sent three of his men to spy out the land. But they didn't return and he went in search of them. At last Odysseus found the men lolling about in a daze and dragged them back to their ships.

The raid on Ismarus

The Greeks plundered the city of Ismarus, helping themselves to treasure and supplies of water, food and wine for their voyage home.

Ask the storyteller

What made Odysseus's men so dozy?

The Lotus-Eaters had given the men the fruit of the lotus plant to eat. It made the men forget all about who they were and their voyage home.

Polyphemus the cyclops

Sailing on, the men reached the land of the cyclopes. Odysseus was eager to find out what these one-eyed giants were like and led a party of men into one of their caves. Soon its owner returned – the gigantic Polyphemus – with one eye staring out from the middle of his forehead. Polyphemus was very angry to find the men in his home and straightaway seized and ate two of them for his supper. Then he made sure the others couldn't escape by blocking the cave's entrance with a huge boulder. The men were terrified, but the wily Odysseus soon worked out a way to escape. The following night, while Polyphemus was asleep, they sharpened a wooden stake and blinded the cyclops with it. In the morning, when Polyphemus rolled away the boulder to let his sheep out, the men sneaked out as well. The enraged cyclops called on the god Poseidon for revenge.

Odysseus tricks the cyclops

In the morning the blinded Polyphemus sat in the cave entrance and felt his sheep's woolly backs to make sure that the men didn't slip out too. He didn't find them though, because they were tied under the sheep's bellies.

Ask the storyteller

Why did Polyphemus ask Poseidon for help?

Polyphemus was one of Poseidon's sons. Poseidon was very angry with Odysseus and vowed to stop the hero from ever returning home.

Keeper of the Winds

Next Odysseus and his men reached the island ruled by King Aeolus, the god of the winds. Aeolus welcomed Odysseus and gave him a mysterious leather bag, which he told him never to open. Then he sent a gentle breeze after the ships to guide them home. But when Odysseus's back was turned, the greedy crew opened the bag, looking for treasure. Out rushed terrible storms, which drove the ships back to the island. This time Aeolus refused to help them. Worse was to come. Setting out again they were blown to the land of the Laestrygonians. There the unfortunate crew met King Antiphates, a man-eating giant, who promptly gobbled up another of Odysseus's men. The rest of the men fled back to their ships, chased by the giants.

The Laestrygonians

The angry Laestrygonians pursued Odysseus's men as they fled back to their ships, hurling boulders and spears at them as they tried to escape. Trapped in the harbour, all the ships were sunk, except Odysseus's.

Circe the enchantress

Mourning their dead friends, Odysseus and his crew sailed on to Circe's island. Upon landing, some of the men went to Circe's house to seek help. Circe was a wicked sorceress, who used her magic to turn men into beasts. All round her house were tame lions and wolves – men who'd been bewitched by Circe. She made Odysseus's men very welcome, but after they'd eaten and drunk her delicious food, she struck them with her wand and turned them into pigs. Only one man, Eurylochus, escaped, as he'd wisely stayed outside. When he saw what had happened to his comrades he rushed back to the ship to warn Odysseus. Odysseus set off at once to confront Circe. On his way he met Hermes, messenger of the gods, who showed the hero how to protect himself against Circe's magic.

Odysseus confronts Circe

When Circe struck Odysseus with her wand, he quickly drew his sword. Fearful that Odysseus meant to kill her, Circe immediately agreed to turn his men back into humans.

Ask the storyteller

How did Hermes protect Odysseus?

Circe secretly mixed a magic potion into the men's food to make them forget where they came from. Hermes gave Odysseus a plant called Moly to put into any food that Circe might offer. This protected him from her magic.

To the Underworld

Circe told Odysseus to visit the Underworld and ask the dead prophet Tiresias how to find his way home. Odysseus was dismayed, for no one ever returned from the Underworld, the home of dead spirits. But he did as Circe instructed. In the Underworld Tiresias warned Odysseus that he'd made an enemy of Poseidon. He told Odysseus that they might still get home safely, as long as they didn't harm the cattle on the Sun God's island. Many other spirits came up to speak to Odysseus, including his mother and his old comrade, the warrior Achilles. Odysseus also saw Sisyphus, who spent his days trying, in vain, to roll a boulder up a mountain as punishment by the gods for his sins. So many wailing spirits pressed round Odysseus that he hurried back to his ship in fear.

Odysseus's mother

Odysseus saw his mother's spirit in the Underworld. He didn't even know that she had died and, overcome by grief, he tried to embrace her. She warned him that, in his absence, his family faced troubles back at home on Ithaca.

96

Ask the storyteller

What were Circe's instructions?

Once in the Underworld, Odysseus had to dig a pit and fill it with the blood of a specially sacrificed ram and a sheep. Only when the dead spirits had drunk from the pit would he be able to speak to them.

Beware Sirens!

Circe was overjoyed when Odysseus returned safely from the Underworld. She wanted to help him, so she gave him instructions on how to avoid the perils that lay ahead. The men soon reached the first of these – the island of the Sirens. The Sirens were part woman, part bird. Their enchanted singing lured all who heard it to their doom on the rocks. Following Circe's advice, Odysseus filled his men's ears with wax so that they wouldn't hear the beautiful songs. Then he ordered his men to bind him tightly to the mast so that he could hear the Sirens, and yet survive. As they rowed near the island Odysseus was so spellbound by the singing that he begged his men to release him. Unable to hear his pleas, the men rowed on as fast as they could and avoided disaster.

Circe's warning

Circe warned Odysseus of the dangers they would find on their way home. After they had passed the Sirens, they would come to the man-eating monster Scylla and Charybdis, a whirlpool that sucked down ships. She urged him to steer a course near Scylla's cave or Charybdis would almost certainly swallow up his crew.

Ask the storyteller

What happened to the Sirens?

Some legends tell that the Sirens hurled themselves off the rocks to their death. They were so upset that Odysseus had not only heard their song, but also lived to warn others about it.

Scylla and Charybdis

Odysseus and his crew arrived at a narrow channel between steep cliffs. On one side lurked the treacherous Charybdis, on the other was the six-headed monster Scylla. Remembering Circe's advice, Odysseus told his terrified men to avoid Charybdis by sailing close to Scylla's cave. Then Odysseus armed himself and prepared to fight Scylla. But the creature was too quick for him. Her six long-necked heads darted in all directions, snatching six of Odysseus's men in her sharp teeth.

When the ship reached the other end of the channel, the men were dazed and exhausted. They decided to rest on the Sun God's island. Despite Odysseus's warning not to harm the grazing cattle, his men disobeyed. Zeus was furious and hurled a thunderbolt at the ship once they'd put to sea again. All the men were drowned, except Odysseus.

The Cattle of the Sun God

Odysseus had not wanted to land on the Sun God's island, but his men were exhausted and begged to rest. They promised not to harm the cattle, but when their food ran out they secretly killed and ate two of them. Remembering Tiresias's warning, Odysseus was horrified.

100

Ask the storyteller

Why did Zeus not punish Odysseus?

The Sun God asked Zeus, the king of the gods, to punish the men for killing his cattle. Odysseus was spared because he was the only one who had not eaten any of the meat.

Calypso and Nausicaa

Odysseus was washed up on the island of the nymph Calypso. All his crew had gone and he was very unhappy. Although he was glad to rest at Calypso's home for a few days, she wanted to keep Odysseus with her forever and wouldn't help him to leave. Feeling sorry for the hero, the gods sent their messenger, Hermes, to the island. After much persuasion, Calypso sadly agreed to let Odysseus go. She helped him make a raft and he soon set sail once again. Poseidon was furious when he saw this and smashed the raft to pieces. For days Odysseus was tossed in stormy seas before reaching the land of the Phaeacians. Here Princess Nausicaa found him and took him to her father's palace. When Odysseus told the Phaeacians his tragic story they gave him one of their ships, filled with gifts, and wished him a safe journey home.

Poseidon's rage

Poseidon was still angry with Odysseus for blinding his son, the cyclops Polyphemus. He was furious with the other gods for helping Odysseus and was determined to stop him from getting home.

Ask the storyteller

How did Nausicaa find Odysseus?

While washing clothes near the sea, Nausicaa and her maids saw Odysseus washed up on shore. After many days at sea Odysseus looked very wild. The maids fled in terror, but the princess treated Odysseus with kindness.

103

Home at last!

Odysseus awoke on yet another beach, not knowing where he was. The Phaeacians' ship had gone and the land was shrouded in mist. Then it cleared, revealing the goddess Athena. When she told the hero that he was home in Ithaca Odysseus kissed the ground, overjoyed to be home at last. But Athena had brought the hero bad news too. She warned him that his life was in danger and told him to seek shelter at the home of his trusty swineherd, Eumaeus, until he'd worked out a plan to destroy his enemies. Athena disguised the hero as an aged beggar so that no-one would recognise him. Grey-haired and leaning on a staff, Odysseus made his way to Eumaeus's hut. Eumaeus did not recognise his old master but greeted the beggar kindly, offering him food and shelter.

Odysseus at Eumaeus's hut

When Odysseus arrived at Eumaeus's hut his dogs bounded out and Eumaeus had to stop them from attacking the old beggar. Odysseus lied about who he was but told the doubting Eumaeus that Odysseus was alive and would soon be home.

Ask the storyteller

Why did Athena send Odysseus to stay with Eumaeus?

Athena wanted to help Odysseus and she knew that Eumaeus was one of the few people that Odysseus could trust.

The suitors of Penelope

In the twenty years that Odysseus had been away, things had not run smoothly on Ithaca. Most people believed that he would never return. For many years Odysseus's beautiful wife Penelope had been plagued by dozens of men eager to marry her and rule the kingdom in Odysseus's place. Penelope still loved Odysseus and didn't want to marry any of these men, but they refused to leave. They hung about the palace, gorging themselves on Odysseus's food and wine. They were also plotting to kill Odysseus's son and heir Telemachus. Telemachus knew that his life was in danger and when Athena instructed him to go to Eumaeus's hut he set off at once. There he was reunited with his long-lost father and together they worked out a plan to get rid of their troublesome enemies.

Penelope's plan

Penelope told the men that she could marry no one until she'd woven a shroud for Odysseus's father, Laertes, who was thought to be dead. Each night she secretly unpicked that day's work to delay her marriage. But a servant betrayed her and the men demanded that she marry one of them immediately.

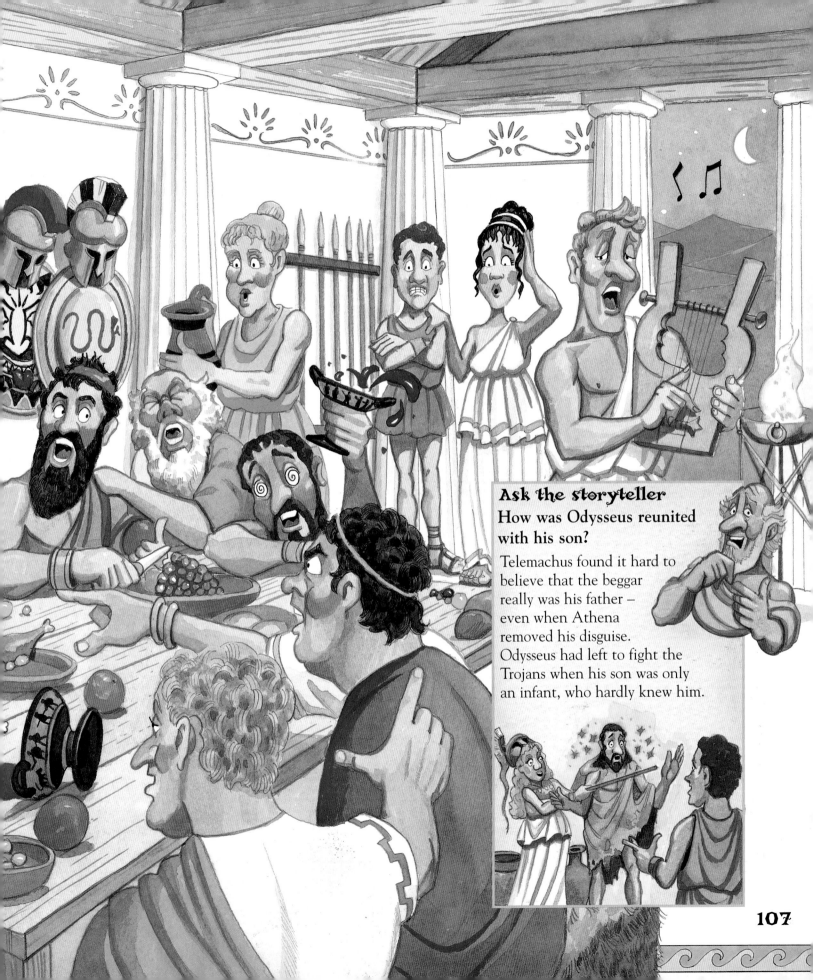

Ask the storyteller
How was Odysseus reunited with his son?

Telemachus found it hard to believe that the beggar really was his father – even when Athena removed his disguise. Odysseus had left to fight the Trojans when his son was only an infant, who hardly knew him.

Jealous rivals

The next morning Odysseus travelled to the palace. He was still disguised as a beggar and only his old dog recognised him. The men jeered when they saw the elderly man and one of them threw a footstool at him. Odysseus was angry but knew that it was not yet the time for revenge. Irus, the brawny palace beggar, was not pleased to see someone else begging there. He challenged Odysseus to a boxing match. Odysseus agreed and astounded everyone by sending Irus sprawling with a single, well-timed blow. That night, when the men had gone home, Odysseus and Telemachus hid all the weapons they had left behind. Odysseus knew that they would be outnumbered in the fight and he would need all his strength and cunning to win. He was still trying to keep his true identity secret, but was recognised by his old nurse Eurycleia.

Ask the storyteller

How did Eurycleia recognise Odysseus?

While washing Odysseus's feet, Eurycleia saw a scar on his leg. It looked just like the one that Odysseus got from boar-hunting as a boy. Odysseus told Eurycleia to keep his secret until he could get rid of his enemies.

Just an old beggar

Penelope did not realise that the old beggar was her husband, Odysseus. She told him that she could no longer wait for her husband to return and must agree to marry another.

A good shot!

The next morning Penelope arranged an archery contest and said that she would marry the winner. The men were delighted, but none of them could even string the great bow which had belonged to Odysseus. They agreed to let the beggar try and to their horror, he won the contest easily. Then, disguised as a swallow, Athena led Odysseus, his son and Eumaeus on to kill all their enemies in a bloody fight. Odysseus revealed his true identity to Penelope and his father Laertes, whom he found working in the fields nearby. The families of the dead were furious with Odysseus and marched to the palace, wanting revenge. Finding the place in an uproar, the goddess Athena persuaded everyone to end their quarrel and live together peacefully again.

Odysseus and his bow

Penelope asked the men to use Odysseus's bow for the contest to test their prowess. To their amazement, the disguised Odysseus bent the great bow easily and won the contest by sending an arrow which pierced twelve axe heads that were lined up in a row.

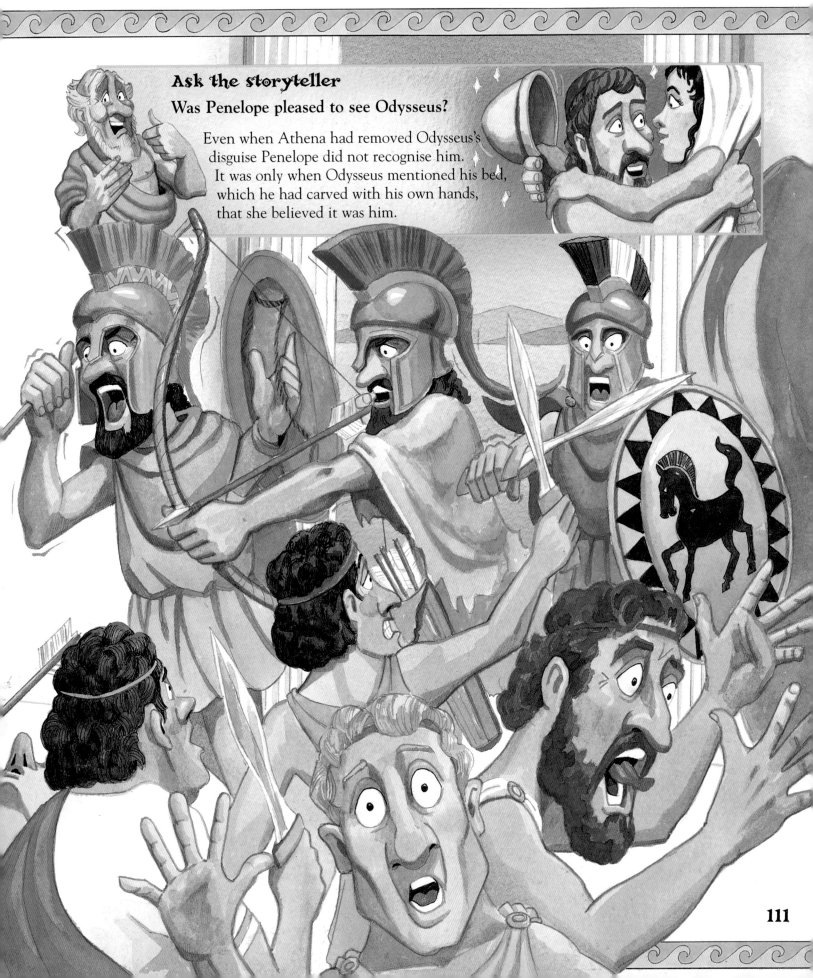

Ask the storyteller

Was Penelope pleased to see Odysseus?

Even when Athena had removed Odysseus's disguise Penelope did not recognise him. It was only when Odysseus mentioned his bed, which he had carved with his own hands, that she believed it was him.

The Adventures of PERSEUS

Meet the heroes

Perseus
The son of the great god Zeus and a mortal princess, baby Perseus was thrown into the sea. Miraculously, he survived...

Polydectes
This prince of Seriphos wants to marry Danae. Perseus doesn't approve, but what can he do about it?

Danae
Princess Danae was so beautiful that Zeus himself fell in love with her. And you can't say no to almighty Zeus!

Andromeda
The beautiful daughter of Queen Cassiopeia is about to be sacrificed to a sea monster. Can our hero save her?

Acrisius
The king of Argos is horrified when an oracle predicts a grim future for him. Can he prevent it from coming true?

Hermes
If Perseus is to succeed, he needs divine help. Fortunately Hermes, the messenger of the gods, decides to take his side.

Introduction

Gather round and hear my story. Is everyone ready? Good, then I shall begin the tale of Perseus, who faced the Gorgon Medusa. But beware, this is not a tale to give you sweet dreams – only nightmares.

We begin in Argos, where King Acrisius was a deeply troubled man. He ruled his kingdom wisely, yet his brother, Proetus, plotted to steal his lands. Faced with such treachery, Acrisius desperately wanted a son – a brave boy to rule Argos after him. Fate had been unkind, however. His only child was a daughter, the beautiful Danae.

Anxiously the King turned to an oracle for help, but was shocked by the prophecy. 'You will never have a son,' she told him 'and your grandson will kill you.' 'No!' yelled Acrisius. 'You are wrong. I won't let it happen. If my daughter never marries, I will have no grandchildren. I'll be safe.'

Gather round and hear my story...

113

The birth of Perseus

Acrisius returned to his palace at once. He commanded the guards to lock poor Danae in a tall bronze tower. 'Why, father?' she sobbed. 'What have I done wrong?'

But even the strongest towers can't keep out the gods. Mighty Zeus heard Danae's cries and fell in love with her. He came to her as a shower of golden rain and she became pregnant. Nine months later she gave birth to a son, Perseus. Terrified of what her father might do, she hid the boy in her bedroom, never allowing him to make a noise.

Danae kept her secret for many months, until one unlucky day Acrisius heard Perseus crying. Wild with anger, he ordered Danae and his grandson to be locked inside a large wooden chest and set afloat on the Aegean Sea. As the chest drifted away Acrisius hoped they would soon drown.

Danae's prison

Chuck them in the sea!

King Acrisius imprisoned Danae in a bronze tower – or did he?
Other versions of this story tell that Danae was locked in a dungeon with bronze doors, guarded by savage dogs. Either way, her jail wasn't strong enough. Zeus still broke in and made her pregnant.

Ask the storyteller

Who was Zeus?

Zeus was the most powerful of the Greek gods. He controlled the skies and the weather, striking his enemies with thunderbolts. He had an eye for a beautiful girl and had several love affairs with mortal women.

Rescued!

Dictys the fisherman was sitting by the rocky shore on the island of Seriphos. He was about to cast his net when something caught his eye. Driftwood? No! A chest, bobbing on the waves like a small boat!

Dictys netted the box and hauled it in, eagerly opening the lid. To his surprise, out climbed an exhausted young woman and her child. When he heard Danae's story, Dictys took pity on the castaways and offered them a home. They lived with him for many happy years and Perseus grew into a sturdy young man. But Danae's good looks were about to get them into trouble again.

One day Polydectes, the king of Seriphos, came to call. He was the brother of Dictys and had fallen in love with Danae. The king decided that she would become his wife. When she refused, he was furious and demanded she obey him. Bristling, Perseus stood guard over his mother and warned the king to leave her alone.

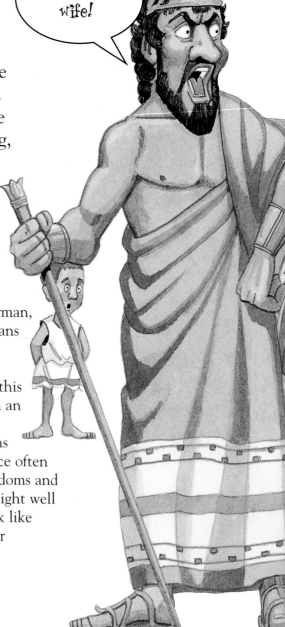

I need a wife!

Dictys the fisherman

Dictys the fisherman, whose name means 'net', was the brother of Polydectes. But this didn't make him an important royal prince. Monarchs in ancient Greece often ruled small kingdoms and their relatives might well do ordinary work like fishing, sailing or making pots.

Polydectes sets a challenge

Frightened by Perseus, Polydectes set out to win Danae by trickery. He announced that he would marry another woman, Hippodamia, and invited all the leading men of the island to a banquet. At the feast he asked them each for a wedding present – 'a love gift' – of a horse. 'Seriphos is only a small island,' he said, 'and I don't want to seem like a beggar compared to other kings who seek the hand of Hippodamia. Will you help me, noble Perseus?'

Perseus was poor, but proud. 'I have no horses or gold, but if you leave my mother alone I will win whatever gift you seek – even the head of the Gorgon, Medusa.'

Polydectes grinned in triumph. The fool had put his neck in the noose. He would never survive a battle with Medusa.

'That would please me more than any horse in the world. Go at once, brave Perseus, and may you soon return safely.'

Who were the Gorgons?

He hasn't got a chance.

The three Gorgons were sisters: Stheno, Euryale and Medusa. Their bodies were covered in scales, their hair writhed with serpents and they had tusks like wild boars. The Gorgons were so ugly that anyone who looked them in the eye turned to stone.

118

Ask the storyteller

Why was Medusa so ugly?

Medusa was once the beautiful lover of Poseidon, god of the sea. One night they slept in a temple dedicated to the goddess Athena, who was so outraged that she turned Medusa into a monster.

A little help from the gods

Overcome with misery, Perseus wandered to a lonely part of Seriphos. 'What chance have I of finding Medusa, let alone killing her?' he sighed. Just then, Athena and the god Hermes appeared. They had watched his encounter with Polydectes and decided to help.

They took Perseus to the Isle of Samos and showed him pictures of the three Gorgons. 'You must be able to recognise Medusa,' Athena warned. 'She is mortal, but her sisters cannot die. If you attack them, they will kill you.' Next they armed Perseus. Hermes gave him a curved crystal sword, tough enough to cut through Medusa's scales, while Athena gave him a shield, so highly polished that it shone like a mirror. 'Use this to seek out your enemy. You can look at her reflection safely, but never gaze directly into her eyes,' the goddess warned.

Athena, warrior goddess

Athena was the guardian of Athens and looked after craftspeople of all kinds. Her father was Zeus and her birth certainly brought him pain. Zeus was suffering from violent headaches, so Hermes sent for Hephaestus, the god of blacksmiths. Swinging his great hammer, Hephaestus struck Zeus on his head. Out of the wound jumped Athena – fully grown and fully armed.

Remember, don't look directly at Medusa. Use this shield instead.

Ask the storyteller
Who was Hermes?

Hermes was the son of Zeus and the goddess Maia. When he was still a baby Hermes stole a herd of cows belonging to Apollo, the god of medicine and music. He made the herd walk backwards so that their tracks left Apollo baffled as he tried to trace them. Seeing Hermes's quick wit, Zeus made him the messenger of the gods and the guardian of roads and travellers.

121

The all-seeing eye

Last of all, Athena and Hermes told Perseus to seek out the Three Grey Women, who lived in a cave at the foot of a huge mountain. They knew how to find the Gorgons and the Stygian Nymphs – if he could make them tell him. 'The Nymphs will prove good friends,' advised Athena. 'Be sure to seek them out before you try to kill Medusa.'

When Perseus tracked down the Grey Women, he was shocked. They were ancient hags who shared one eye and one tooth between them. Stealthily, he crept behind them and awaited his chance. As the single eye and tooth were passed from one hag to another, Perseus leapt out and seized them, leaving the women blind and squealing with rage. 'If you want these back, tell me the way to the Nymphs and to your evil sisters' hiding place,' he ordered. Helpless, they had no choice but to tell Perseus everything.

The Old Ones

The Grey Women were also known as the 'Graeae' or 'Old Ones' because their hair was grey from birth. Strangely, in some myths they are described as swan-like and beautiful, rather than ugly crones.

The Stygian Nymphs

The Stygian Nymphs welcomed Perseus kindly and gave him three gifts – tools for his battle with the Gorgons. The first gift was a pair of winged sandals, like those worn by Hermes himself, the second a magical helmet and the last, a silver *kibisis*, or pouch. Putting on the sandals Perseus laughed in delight – they gave him the power of flight.

Thanking the Nymphs, he soared into the sky, like a falcon seeking its prey. The Grey Women had told him that Medusa lived in Hyperborea, the Land of the North Winds. After a long journey Perseus landed near the Gorgons' lair. He shuddered at what he found. All around him were the bodies of men and beasts, turned into stone by the malevolent gaze of Medusa. Remembering Athena's warning, Perseus fixed his eyes on the reflection in his shield and set about his task.

The Cap of Darkness

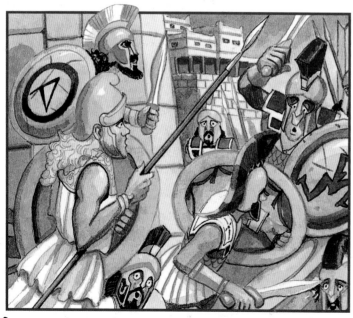

The magical helmet was called the Cap of Darkness. In the Trojan War between the Greece and Troy, the goddess Athena herself fought on the side of the Greeks. When she first went into battle she was wearing the magical helmet that was later given to Perseus.

Ask the storyteller

What powers did the other gifts bring?

Together with the flying sandals, the Nymphs gave Perseus other vital equipment. The Cap of Darkness made the wearer invisible and the silver pouch changed size to hold whatever was put inside it.

Perseus faces Medusa

Luckily for Perseus, the Gorgons were asleep and he was able to creep in amongst the hideous sisters. Using the shield, he identified Medusa and took aim with the crystal sword. 'Steady now,' he whispered to himself, 'you won't get a second chance.' But his aim was true and with one fierce blow Perseus beheaded his foe. Bending to pick up her writhing head, he thrust it in the pouch. The serpents hissed in outrage as the darkness closed over them.

The next moments were filled with horror. Unknown to Perseus, Medusa was pregnant with Poseidon's children. As she died she gave birth to Pegasus, a winged horse, and Chrysaor the warrior, armed with a golden sword. Wailing at the fate of their mother, the newborns woke their aunts, Stheno and Euryale. Perseus turned to flee.

The Gorgons' lament

Athena had a cruel sense of humour. She heard Stheno and Euryale wailing over the death of Medusa and gleefully invented the flute to mimic the sound of their grief. Athena gave this new instrument to humans and called it 'the music of many heads'.

Hisss
Hisssss
Hisss
Hisss

Ask the storyteller

How did Perseus escape?

Perseus couldn't kill Stheno and Euryale, so he had to run – or rather fly – for his life. But the Gorgons flew after him. Perseus only escaped because he became invisible when he pulled on the Cap of Darkness.

The curse of Atlas

Perseus flew south until strong winds blew him off course and he stopped to rest in the lands ruled by Atlas the Titan. Atlas was a god of immense strength whom no-one dared to cross. A thousand herds of cattle safely roamed his lands and thieves stayed well away from the golden apples that grew in his orchards.

Perseus asked for a night's shelter and did his best to impress the Titan. 'If a noble family counts, I am the son of almighty Zeus.' It was a boast best left unsaid. Atlas had been warned by an oracle that his apples would be stolen by a son of his old enemy, Zeus. 'Away! Be gone!' the Titan ordered. 'There is no welcome for you here.'

Deeply insulted, Perseus wrestled with Atlas and pulled Medusa's head from the pouch. As the Titan stared into her dead eyes he was turned into the range of mountains – the Atlas Mountains – that still bears his name today.

Who was Atlas?

Atlas was a Titan, one of the older gods who ruled the earth before it was taken over by Zeus and the newer gods from Mount Olympus. Atlas led the Titans in a ten-year war against Zeus and only lost because the Cyclopes, one-eyed master craftsmen, made deadly weapons for the Olympians, like Zeus's thunderbolts.

Get out, son of Zeus!

Ask the storyteller
What happened to Atlas?

In Greek mythology Atlas is about as unlucky as you can get. He was singled out by Zeus for special punishment and ordered to hold the world on his back. After Perseus turned him into a mountain range, he still didn't get any rest. It is said the 'vault of heaven' rested on his summits.

Andromeda and the sea monster

Perseus set out for home along the coast of Africa. Turning north across Philistia, he flew over a pitiful scene – a young woman chained to the rocky shore. Zooming down for a closer look he saw that she was strikingly beautiful and fell instantly in love with her.

A wailing crowd stood on the beach nearby and Perseus landed beside them. 'Who is that girl?' he demanded. 'Who dares treat her like this?' Her mother Cassiopeia and her father Cepheus stepped nervously forward. 'We are the rulers of this land,' they cried. 'Poseidon, lord of the sea, has sent a monster to punish us. We have to sacrifice our daughter to the beast – or we will all die.' At once Perseus vowed to rescue Andromeda and in return her parents agreed that he could marry her and take her back to Greece.

Cassiopeia's boast

Queen Cassiopeia, like her daughter Andromeda, was very good-looking. The Queen had boasted that they were so attractive they even outshone the Nereids. This was a big mistake! The Nereids were beautiful mermaids and they complained bitterly to Poseidon about this insult from a mere mortal.

Ask the storyteller

Why was Cepheus willing to sacrifice his daughter?

To punish Cassiopeia for her vanity, Poseidon sent a terrible sea monster to devastate Philistia. Cepheus had asked an oracle what he should do. He was told the only hope of saving his country was to feed his daughter to the monster.

Is anyone brave enough to save me?

The jealousy of Agenor

Drawing his crystal sword Perseus hovered over the sea, determined to stop the monster. However, as he dived down, the creature snapped at him and kept him at bay. Then, Perseus remembered he had the Cap of Darkness. As the serpent surged towards Andromeda, Perseus, invisible and undetected, struck a fierce blow and cut off its head.

Now that she was safe, Perseus unchained Andromeda and carried her ashore. Eager to marry her brave hero, she asked for the wedding to take place straight away. The crowd cheered and the celebrations had just begun, when Agenor arrived with an armed gang of over two hundred men. He was Andromeda's old boyfriend who had come to claim her for himself. Perseus fought bravely but he was hopelessly outnumbered.

Set in the stars

Cassiopeia turned against Perseus as soon as the monster was dead. She said that he couldn't marry Andromeda because she was already engaged. Even worse, Cassiopeia sent a message to Agenor: 'Come at once – Perseus must die!' To punish her for this betrayal Poseidon set her picture in the stars. The constellation of Cassiopeia shows her tied up in a market-basket.

Ask the storyteller

What happened to Agenor?

In the battle on the beach, Agenor was sure he would take Andromeda from Perseus. But he didn't know what was in Perseus's pouch. With no other way to save himself and his bride, Perseus pulled out Medusa's head and turned Agenor and his gang into stone.

He was there a moment ago...

Perseus rescues his mother

Taking Andromeda with him Perseus flew back to the island of Seriphos. He found his mother and was outraged to discover that Polydectes had lied. The king was trying to force Danae into marriage again. Perseus stormed into the palace where Polydectes was holding a banquet. 'Here is your wedding present!' he announced, flinging down the pouch. He was met with a chorus of jeers and insults from the king and his cronies. 'It's impossible to slay a Gorgon. You are a liar!' they yelled.

Wild with anger, Perseus reached into the pouch. Since no-one believed he had killed Medusa, no-one tried to stop him. Pulling out the dreadful head, he swung it in an arc around the room. All who looked into the terrible eyes of Medusa turned into stone. Perseus walked away, leaving the petrified king and his courtiers in their stoney silence.

Refuge in the temple

To escape Polydectes, Danae and Dictys had taken refuge in a temple while Perseus had been away. The King was frightened to drag them out in case he angered one of the gods. After Perseus had dealt with King Polydectes he rewarded Dictys's loyalty to Danae by making him king of Seriphos.

Ask the storyteller

What happened to Medusa's head?

With his mother safe, Perseus's task was done. Athena gratefully accepted the head of Medusa as a gift and hung it on her shield. The Gorgon's head became one of Athena's symbols.

The death of Acrisius

Perseus now looked forward to a quiet life. Together with his mother and Andromeda, he set sail for Argos. His grandfather Acrisius, who had sealed him in the wooden chest so many years ago, heard of their return and fled to the city of Larissa.

Soon, however, Perseus was to follow him there by chance. He simply went to compete in the funeral games that the King of Larissa was holding in honour of his dead father. Perseus took part in the discus and threw with all his strength and skill. But the wind sprang up and the gods struck again. His discus blew off course, hitting the foot of an old spectator, killing him instantly. To everyone's astonishment, it turned out to be Acrisius!

Fate catches up with Acrisius

Acrisius was terrified when he heard that Perseus was coming back to Argos. The oracle had foretold his death and surely, the old man thought, his grandson was coming to kill him. Little did he know that Perseus had forgiven him and only wanted to become friends. Tragically, when Acrisius ran away he set the scene for the oracle's prophecy to come true.

Ask the storyteller
How did Perseus feel?

Perseus was so ashamed that he had killed his grandfather that instead of returning to Argos to become King, he swapped lands with his cousin, the King of Tiryns. Perseus ruled Tiryns for many happy years, with Andromeda by his side.

A strong boy like that would make a father proud.

Glossary

Abducted Taken away against one's will.

Amazons A race of warrior women.

Ambassador An official sent to talk to the leaders of a foreign country.

Blacksmith Metalworker.

Centaur A mythical creature which was half-man, half-horse.

Channel A narrow stretch of water between two land masses.

Constellation A group of stars that shows an image in the night sky.

Crone An ugly old woman.

Cyclops A cave-dwelling giant with only one eye.

Duel A fight between two people.

Elysian fields The Greek version of heaven.

Epic A long poem about war and the deeds of heroes.

Figurehead The decorative statue attached to the front of a ship.

Girdle A type of belt.

Groom Someone who looks after horses.

Harpy A flying creature with a woman's head and the body, wings and claws of a bird.

Heir A person who will gain the possessions and titles of someone when they die.

Immobilise To make something unable to move.

Immortal A being who cannot die, such as a god.

Inherit To receive wealth or a title from someone when they die.

Invulnerable Unable to be harmed.

Kibisis A magical silver pouch that changes to hold what is put inside it.

Krotala A special rattle made for Heracles by the god Hephaestus.

Lame Unable to walk.

Lotus A plant whose fruit made people dreamy and forgetful.

Lyre A stringed musical instrument popular in Ancient Greece.

Malevolent Wishing to do harm.

Moly A magical herb with a black root and white flower.

Mortal A being who will die one day, or who can be killed.

Mount Olympus The mountain on which the gods were thought to live.

Nereid A nymph who lives in the sea.

Nymph A spirit in the shape of a beautiful young woman.

Oath A solemn promise.

Omen A sign which predicts future events.

Oracle A place where you go to hear what will happen in the future.

Orchard A place where fruit trees grow.

Pelt The skin of a dead animal.

Petrified Extremely frightened, or turned into stone.

Philistia A country in the Middle East, now part of Israel.

Pilgrim A person who goes on a journey for religious reasons.

Pithos A large jar for storing food.

Prophecy A prediction of what will happen in the future.

Prophet Someone who tells a prophecy.

Prowess Skill or strength.

Pyre A platform on which corpses are burnt.

Quiver A container for arrows.

Ransom A payment for the safe return of a prisoner.

Ravenous Very hungry.

Sacrifice To kill a creature or person as a gift to a god.

Sacrilege A crime against the gods.

Shrine A special place to worship the gods.

Shroud A sheet in which a dead body is wrapped.

Siren A flying creature with a woman's head and a bird's body, whose beautiful singing lured sailors to their doom on the rocky coast.

Soothsayer A person who uses observations of nature to predict the future.

Sorceress A female magician who uses magic to bewitch people.

Styx A river in the Underworld.

Suitor A man who is seeking a woman's hand in marriage.

Swineherd A person who looks after pigs.

Temple A place of worship. Most gods had temples built in their honour.

Titan One of a race of giant gods overthrown by Zeus.

Trojan War A war between the Greeks and the city of Troy, because a Trojan Prince stole the wife of a Greek king.

Truce An agreement to stop fighting.

Underworld The place where Ancient Greeks believed that people went after they died.

Vanquished Overcome by force.

Index